W9-AXQ-808

HOW TO BEDEVIL A BUSINESS

William A. Stanmeyer, J.D.

HOW TO BEDEVIL A BUSINESS

By William A. Stanmeyer, J.D.

Published by Lincoln Communications Corporation. Printed in the United States of America by Good Printers, Inc., Bridgewater, Virginia.

Cover design by Tom Richardson

First Edition, May 2000

ISBN: 0-9650992-1-0

DEDICATION

This book is dedicated to

all my friends in

an extraordinary business,

who have the courage to help others

achieve their dreams.

INTRODUCTION

In every genre of imaginative writing, whether mystery, spy, or science fiction novel, the reader must grant the author his premise.

From Arthur Conan Doyle, to Ian Fleming, to Isaac Asimov and beyond, fiction writers have given their heroes preternatural powers of logical thinking, martial arts, or resourceful courage. Often they place the story in strange or exotic locales: remote mansions in mist-shrouded fens, planets in other galaxies.

The writers do not ask the reader to *believe* such heroes or places exist; but they do ask suspension of doubt. For the sake of the story, *pretend* that they are real.

This is not a matter of metaphysics or theology, but simply of customary literary license. For the sake of enjoying the story, its persons and places are *deemed to be real*, not in the actual world of course, but *in the story*.

So the author and the reader enter a kind of compact: they agree to share the pretense that setting and characters are real, so that they can enjoy what transpires before their eyes. Here, the literary device in *How to Bedevil* is one less widely used; but the author and the reader must enter the same compact.

The pretense of imaginary "letters" from a devil in hell to a subordinate on earth is not original. The witty, incisive, and profound *Screwtape Letters*, by C.S. Lewis over fifty years ago, was a brilliant archetype and model for all later imitators.

As Lewis conceived him, Screwtape had to endure his bungling subordinate Wormwood up on earth, in order to lead a particular individual and his family to spiritual perdition.

In the story that follows, Shrewdtrap, Senior Consultant, Department of Demonomics, has much the same burden: to put up with Warmwart, an inferior up on earth as inept as Wormwood. The cause: leading a particular individual and his family to financial perdition.

Thus Shrewdtrap endures Warmwart's incessant mistakes, as he tries to educate him in the fine art of causing financial failure. Like his predecessor, Shrewdtrap is embodied malice, intelligent, persistent, focussed. Unfortunately for his plans, his agent-in-the-field, Warmwart, is not.

Through Shrewdtrap's reverse-image viewpoint, the reader may obtain a new perspective on the challenges of a referral-based business in the E-Commerce era. But a caution: Shrewdtrap *could* be lying, even to Warmwart. And like all finite beings, he can be wrong. He is intelligent, not infallible. So, discern the spirits.

Finally, though this work is fiction, Shrewdtrap's traps deserve the attention of the reader for another reason: he may run into them himself-- in the real world.

William A. Stanmeyer

From: Shrewdtrap@hellnet.edu
To: Warmwart@worldtrick.com
Subject: The Importance of Causing Financial Failure

My dear Warmwart:

So you were surprised at your transfer, were you? You say you should put your supposed talents to the service of tempting humans to commit sin, but that spending time tempting them to fail *in a business* is a waste of good fiendpower.

You seem to think that we at the Low Command have made a *mistake* in your reassignment! You should know by now that we do not make mistakes! As Our Father Below taught us from the beginning, we have *never* made a mistake.

That self-evident fact is an *apriori*, a given. So it logically follows that your transfer is a good idea: it will help to further the Cause. If your dim wits were sharper, you could figure this out yourself.

As Senior Consultant here, normally I do not waste my time explaining an Order to stupid subordinates. But on the outside chance that an explanation might stoke your fervor in the Cause to a hotter degree, I will explain...

You say you do not understand why we promote human failure, since success produces money--and the love of money is the root of all evil. The answer is that the Joint Chiefs of the Low Command agreed on three main reasons for keeping humans in involuntary poverty.

First--surely, Warmwart, having dealt with humans for a few eons now, you must have been disgusted whenever you came across one that was actually *happy*. Did you notice that money--wealth--financial freedom--usually contributes to their happiness?

Notice I said *contributes*. The humans have a saying, "Money can't buy happiness," which strictly speaking is true; but having a bit of money can remove many material causes of unhappiness. If a person has a toothache, money to pay the dentist will dispel his pain. If a man earns enough money, his wife can stay home to raise the children.

Obviously, we want the toothache to get worse and both wife and husband to work as much as possible away from home.

Second, when a human has money other bad consequences follow; e.g., he might give ten percent to charity. If he earns $100,000, then $10,000 goes to some charity that we oppose.

But if he earns, say, a mere $20,000, he may not even give $2,000. So, by holding his income down, we deprive some "good causes" of good money.

Third, the Enemy wants humans to prosper. Of course, He connects prosperity of body and prosperity of soul: Greed, one of the finest of vices, is condemned; gratitude for blessings, not Pride in one's own achievements, is insisted upon.

Needless to say, if we detect any such pernicious virtues blossoming in the soil of a wealthy man's heart, we must cut them out at the root: only then would his wealth be to our advantage.

But since most humans start in relative poverty, it is easier to keep them there and then crush their spirit in this world as a prelude to crushing it in the next.

So, the goal of *your* assignment is to keep your human targets from financial success. Frustrate their natural dreams. Disappoint their legitimate expectations. Confuse them about money, so they feel guilty if they make any significant amounts.

If you are as clever as I, in some cases you may even nurture feelings of *Pride* in their confused hearts! Yes, Pride at being poor: they will feel they are "better" than people they know who have money!

> Your affectionate Mentor,
> Shrewdtrap, S.C.
> Department of Demonomics

From: Shrewdtrap@hellnet.edu
To: Warmwart@worldtrick.com
Subject: The Basis for Financial Success

My dear Warmwart:

Your failures on prior assignments were due to your shallow grasp of fundamentals. When one sets out to accomplish any work, he needs to understand the basics. Since your task is to prevent human financial success, you need to know its essentials.

The only significant difference between a human and a pig or a porpoise is that the former has a *mind*.

Pigs and porpoises, cats and crows--and all other non-rational animals--eat and drink and sleep and wake. So do humans. But the animals never achieve financial success. Humans sometimes do.

The difference between pigs and porpoises, cats and crows, men and women is not in their muscles; it is in their minds. So obviously financial success is not due to strength of body but to clarity of mind: *wealthy people think differently from the non-wealthy.*

Generally, every successful person thinks the way most other successful people think. Similarly, every failure thinks the way most other failures think. *But no successful person thinks like a failure, and no failure thinks like a successful person.*

You must study successful people, Warmwart, identify the way they think, and make it your purpose to discourage your targets from imitating those successful people. Having done this for eons, I can give you a hint:

Keep them from even *associating* with successful people. Attitudes rub off.

Your affectionate Mentor,
Shrewdtrap, S.C.
Department of Demonomics

3

From: Shrewdtrap@hellnet.edu
To: Warmwart@worldtrick.com
Subject: Goals

My dear Warmwart:

You've been in the U.S. for awhile now. Have you learned anything?

For example, did you ever wonder why a Korean or Vietnamese immigrant, new to the country, with scarcely any money and no knowledge of the language, manages to buy a small store somewhere and, within a few years, makes it into a successful business?

The answer: they have a *goal*. They have a burning desire to achieve something. Their goal is specific. They visualize exactly what they want, and the vision carries them over every obstacle.

All human achievement starts with a vision. Everything in their world that is worthwhile is a "dream come true": the low-ball handicap, the fine building replacing an empty lot, the graduate's diploma. In every case, they had to imagine what they wanted before they achieved it.

"What the human mind can conceive and believe, it can achieve." Human beings *become* what they think about. This is surely true for human athletes: every day the would-be Olympian thinks and breathes, eats and sleeps his goal of qualifying for the Olympics.

Success is the progressive realization of a worthwhile goal. This means that without a worthy goal, a human cannot succeed.

Those who drift through life, taking their cues from those around them, have not bothered to stop, clarify their goals, write them down, and every day study what they have written.

Your goal, Warmwart, when you deal with some human who might wander into the promised land of success, is to keep them confused about goals. That is *your* goal. Better write it down.

Your affectionate Mentor,
Shrewdtrap, S.C.
Department of Demonomics

4

From: Shrewdtrap@hellnet.edu
To: Warmwart@worldtrick.com
Subject: The Target

My dear Warmwart:

You say you have run across a human couple, a man named Frank and his wife Jennifer, to practice on. *Practice!* ye gods, Warmwart, you should know by now that ruining humans in the Game of Life is not played in *practice!*

I'll let the word pass, on the assumption that you mean it the way human lawyers or doctors speak about "the practice of law" or "the practice of medicine": they seriously do a professional job, but they learn as they go.

Now, to the main point... Yes, practice--professionally do a job--on Frank and Jennifer. Analyze the tensions in their marital relationship to see where you can exploit them. But learn as you go.

Look at their jobs and the time they spend away from each other and from their children. Try to convince them that long hours out of the home is "what everybody does these days": it's the natural arrangement. Tell them the idea of Mom staying home with the children is old fashioned.

You say she is inclined to start some sort of home-based business. My guess is, she would not be thinking along these lines unless she is dissatisfied with the *status quo*. You must be careful here. Remember, virtue usually stands in the middle. So you must push them toward one of two extremes.

On the one hand, if they are "time-bankrupt," get them so frustrated with their situation that they finally chuck it all, quit their jobs and, without advice from anyone who knows what he's doing, mindlessly start a full-time business that--with your help--fails dismally, leaving them worse off than before.

On the other hand, you can work to persuade them to stay in their rut. Keep them there until it becomes a rut with an end to it: a grave.

5

The last thing you want them to do is pursue a part-time business that does not disrupt their lives while still does provide them hope of eventual escape from the rut.

Your affectionate Mentor,
Shrewdtrap, S.C.
Department of Demonomics

From: Shrewdtrap@hellnet.edu
To: Warmwart@worldtrick.com
Subject: Targets' Biog

My dear Warmwart:

    You have targeted a certain Frank and Jennifer. Your last E-mail stated that they are in their mid-30s; he is a trial lawyer, and she works in corporate advertising; they have a three-year-old son named Tommy and she is pregnant with Number Two.

    You say Frank earns a six-figure income and that Jennifer's job adds luxuries but goes mostly to pay an all-day babysitter, a reliable Hispanic named Maria. Frank works twelve hour days; he is stressed, especially by the lack of exercise. Jennifer is discontented that she sees her husband and child so little.

    There should be potential here for all sorts of mischief: increase the pressures on Frank so that he constantly annoys his wife with his peevishness; introduce Jennifer to some "liberated woman" who counsels her to leave Frank--she hardly ever sees him anyway; find a way to get rid of Maria and replace her with someone unreliable.

    There would be potential--*but*--you say she has taken note of the fault lines in their relationship and wonders whether a home-based business of some kind could help them out of their rut.

    At this point, she is going down the wrong path. You must keep him from joining her.

    For humans rather firmly set in their careers, this is an unlikely insight. Did she come upon this idea on her own, or has some independent thinker entered their lives?

                   Your affectionate Mentor,
                   Shrewdtrap, S.C.
                   Department of Demonomics

From: Shrewdtrap@hellnet.edu
To: Warmwart@worldtrick.com
Subject: Alert! Counterattack McDermott

My dear Warmwart:

I thought so--it was an independent thinker. You say a new neighbor, a man named McDermott, at a recent community association meeting, in response to Frank's half brag/half complaint about his long hours, remarked that "On his death bed a man never says, 'I wish I'd spent more time at the office.'"

By hell, Warmwart, for a husband who burns the candle at both ends, these should be fighting words! That was your chance to create permanent animosity between those men: you should have whispered to Frank, "Shut up, you *&^%$#@! It's none of your damn business how much time I spend at the office!"

That's what an alert Tempter would say--and make him think this was *his* thought, not yours. Make him say it out loud, if you can, so that his new friend beats a hasty retreat or, better yet, fires back an insult of his own.

Instead, you stood idly by as Frank's better side took over and he lamely commented, "Not much a guy can do about it--it's the Rat Race we all run."

I won't recount all the dialogue you reported. The key was McDermott's response: "That used to be the case, but with the Internet today it's possible for any professional to have a side business that is lucrative enough to cut back his hours at the office." That tweaked Frank's curiosity.

So Frank and McDermott agreed to meet next Saturday to go over this Internet business, and, if Frank found it interesting, maybe arrange to attend a business seminar next week.

Warmwart, don't you see what's coming? This McDermott fellow has targeted *your* target! Worse still, depending on his purpose, he may give *good* advice!

8

Hie thee over to Frank and Jennifer right away. Talk them out of "wasting an afternoon" with a virtual stranger. Appeal to his--or her--status: attorneys often feel they are smarter than ordinary mortals, so whisper that McDermott couldn't *possibly* teach *them* anything valuable about making money.

Your affectionate Mentor,
Shrewdtrap, S.C.
Department of Demonomics

From: Shrewdtrap@hellnet.edu
To: Warmwart@worldtrick.com
Subject: Learn Motivation from Your Opponents!

My dear Warmwart:

You say your targets are "open-minded." Another bad sign, Warmwart! Also, they're smart enough to realize that though McDermott is not an attorney, he might know something about making money that Frank does not.

They noticed that Steve McDermott enjoys plenty of time at home with his wife and kids and yet manages to live in the same nice neighborhood they do.

You suggested to Frank that McDermott, being only a former IBM middle manager, couldn't possibly teach *him* anything. What could a tech guy, who used to sit in front of a screen all day, teach a high-powered attorney about making money?

That was fine, Warmwart, but you pushed too far. You pressed the thought so forcefully that Frank said it out loud to Jennifer. Rather than let the objection fester quietly in his mind, you exposed it to immediate rebuttal!

She simply asked him, "If you're so smart, Mr. Big Shot Attorney, why don't you ever have time to work out?" But she was clever enough to say it in a cheerful, friendly way, so he did not blow up. Then, while you were sicklied over with the pale cast of thought, she won the point.

"You *are* smart enough to see through a scam when you see one. Why don't you sit down with him and be an adversary: pick apart his idea, show him it won't work, and then you'll feel better not doing it. Might do him a favor, too!"

This is verbal jui-jitsu: she took his desire--time--and his pride--he is a tough lawyer--and leveraged him into agreeing to meet with McDermott. She got what she wanted. It may be that the only profit you gain from this assignment is to learn from the humans how to motivate people!

> Your affectionate Mentor,
> Shrewdtrap, S.C.
> Department of Demonomics

From: Shrewdtrap@hellnet.edu
To: Warmwart@worldtrick.com
Subject: [See Text Below]

My dear Warmwart:

You haven't filed your weekly report. Submit it immediately, or you will be recalled for corrective retraining at one of our brimstone camps!

> Your affectionate Mentor,
> Shrewdtrap, S.C.
> Department of Demonomics

From: Shrewdtrap@hellnet.edu
To: Warmwart@worldtrick.com
Subject: Attack the Messenger

My dear Warmwart:

Serphide has e-mailed me an urgent Memo on your targets' recent activities. He states you have failed to inform me that the speaker at that "opportunity meeting" they attended described the rewards of a successful small business.

The speaker described his home with paneled library, gym/exercise room in the basement, rec. room with a pool table, and large outdoor swimming pool.

He said he wakes up at 9:30 a.m., plays with his pre-school children, has a light breakfast with his wife, takes a three-mile walk, returns to his home office to handle phone calls and pay bills--adding that he has no debt--then works out for an hour in his private gym.

You hovered there in the room all along, watching this sickening depiction of a lifestyle that most Americans, even those with high incomes, never have time to enjoy.

How did Frank and Jennifer react? Envy? Disbelief? Anger that no one had, until then, offered this to them? Eagerness to learn more and perhaps emulate the speaker?

What did they think of this litany of comforts? I hope they were put off by it, since one way to deflect them from starting a small business that might create great prosperity is to twist their thinking about prosperity itself.

The next time at one of these meetings, whisper that the speaker is "materialistic"--that *they*, Frank and Jennifer, would never spend so much money on *themselves*, the way he did. Add that he could not be a good man if he has so much time on his hands, and so much money to spend.

Make them feel vaguely superior to him, and thus "above" the business he summarized.

11

I call this technique *the reverse ad-hominem attack*: attack the messenger, since the message is what is important. Who cares how the speaker spends his money? The issue for Frank and Jennifer was, What can this program do for Frank and Jennifer?

The speaker could give all his income to Mother Theresa's nuns! It would not matter.

Again, as long as the business is honest, the *speaker's* use of *his own* money should be irrelevant to the merits of how he made it. The only issue for Frank and Jennifer is how Frank and Jennifer would use the money if they made it.

I assume the speaker was truthful: he stated that the business brought good money and more time back into his life. You must distract them from that truth: sidetrack them with irrelevancies such as the speaker's use of his own money!

Heed my words or, by Beelzebub, I'll see you chin-deep in molten lava. Try to conjure up a smidgen of malevolent initiative. Don't let realism about time and money slip into their minds; put your own really false ideas in.

Your affectionate Mentor,
Shrewdtrap, S.C.
Department of Demonomics

From: Shrewdtrap@hellnet.edu
To: Warmwart@worldtrick.com
Subject: Referral-Based Private Franchising

My dear Warmwart:

Unbeknownst to you, I dispatched Serphide, Scumslip, and Slantcreep to the United States to reconnoiter. They informed me about what is involved here: a business that uses interactive and referral-based distribution and has recently added an Internet website.

Because you have not been briefed on this before, I will summarize its strengths and weaknesses.

If you cannot stop Frank and Jennifer, McDermott will "sponsor" or "register" them. He will "franchise" them, as it were, to buy products at a discount, refer others to the website, and sign up additional new people in turn.

They will earn commissions on everything anyone "below" them purchases, through this referral-based system. This includes everyone later brought in by their referrals, or successive ones after those.

The financial attraction is the possibility of exponential expansion: if Frank sponsors half-a-dozen people, and they all bring in another six, that's 36. If these each sign in six in turn, the group is up to 216. Then, when each of the 216 "franchise" six more, the total is 1,296.

Should the average person purchase $100.00 per month in products, Frank and Jennifer would then have a business doing $129,600.00 per month, or over $1,500,000 per year. Depending on the bonus formula, this volume might produce a six-figure income.

This simple theory is brilliant. The practice is more complicated. Many who join do not realize such growth is not automatic: a person must work. It takes time.

But they get frustrated easily. Remember, we have taught them impatience if the stop light stays red longer than a minute or the microwave fails to produce hot soup in thirty seconds.

13

So do not argue with Frank and Jennifer that this idea does not work in theory. He will see through that lie.

Instead, make *him* experience it "not working" with the first few people he approaches. As early prospects, steer people toward him who are lazy, egotistical, allergic to success, who cannot "think outside the box" and recognize a good business when they see one.

When these people say No, or laugh at him, or state--without a shred of evidence--that "It won't work," they will frustrate Frank so much that he may well quit.

Remember, attorneys cannot stand rejection. They think they have to "win" in every encounter.

> Your affectionate Mentor,
> Shrewdtrap, S.C.
> Department of Demonomics

From: Shrewdtrap@hellnet.edu
To: Warmwart@worldtrick.com
Subject: Some Bullets

My dear Warmwart:

You have to be more creative. You bother me with E-mails to ask about every single tactic you might try. For hell's sake, Warmwart, just go out and *do* something, anything, rather than mope around paralyzed while your target wanders toward success because you could conjure up no quick move to deflect him.

Now, to the point: you asked for ideas to insinuate into his mind that might end his flirtation with this new business venture. I will give some.

First, say--get him to say to McDermott--"It sounds like a good idea, but *I just don't have time.*" Remind him he already works 70 to 80 hours a week.

Or, slip into his mother-in-law's mind the thought, which she will say to him because she can't keep from giving unsolicited advice on things she knows nothing about, "You are a successful *lawyer.* A man in your position shouldn't demean himself by getting into a business *like that.*"

Third, get at him through Jennifer. The way to nip a good idea in the bud is to refocus on the obstacles they will bump into in pursuit of it. Get her mind off staying home with the kids and seeing Frank more. Make her think about how much *more* time he will be away, in the evenings, building this business.

Fire all three shots at once. Even with your poor aim, one should hit the target.

                        Your affectionate Mentor,
                        Shrewdtrap, S.C.
                        Department of Demonomics

From: Shrewdtrap@hellnet.edu
To: Warmwart@worldtrick.com
Subject: How to Aim Straight

My dear Warmwart:

Don't blame *me* because *you* could not shoot a gun straight that I had loaded. Let me go back over the drill one more time.

First, you did get Frank to remark to McDermott, "I just don't have time." But McDermott was prepared; without missing a beat, he answered: "That's exactly why you *do* need this business! It will give you time. You'll be just as busy five, ten years from now--but with less energy."

Were *you* ready with a rejoinder? Or did you stand there and fume-- but say nothing? Reading between the lines of your last E-mail, it seems you said nothing.

It is disgusting that a human, with an intellect even dimmer than yours, plans his verbal moves further in advance than *you* do. I am glad this game is not chess: you'd be in checkmate by the third move!

Second, Frank's mother-in-law did make the comment you suggested. But--something you had not warned me about--Frank had long ago written her opinions off. In fact, with an attorney's typical self-assurance, he makes it a point to do the *opposite* of her counsel. So this tack did not billow our sails.

The Attack-by-Trojan-Horse-Family-Member works if the target has a weak self-image and is more worried about what people who do not pay his bills think, than about paying them. Keep this in mind for the future.

Third, what about Jennifer? Your letter is silent about her. Did you transplant mental myopia into her thinking, so that the immediate obstacles loomed so large she lost sight of the long-term goal?

Your affectionate Mentor,
Shrewdtrap, S.C.
Department of Demonomics

From: Shrewdtrap@hellnet.edu
To: Warmwart@worldtrick.com
Subject: Good and Bad Multilevel

My dear Warmwart:

You say this business model uses "multilevel marketing" methods and that you have discovered many Americans have earned good money through it, but some others think it is a scam. You ask how both can be true.

You need clear thinking here, Warmwart. Your puzzlement sounds like the muddle we have promoted for forty years in human minds. Confuse the humans; don't confuse yourself.

Here is the answer: first, the system is valid and legal, if it meets legal rules. For example: no recruitment fees, just for bringing someone in; real products must really be moved--no "chain letter" device is permitted; it is not just a wholesale buying club: to earn commissions one must have a few customers.

The key is point is: the thing must be run as a legitimate business.

Second, now and then people--usually under our astute tutelage, I can add proudly--set up business ventures on this model. But in their greed, they try to squeeze big dollars out up front, even if the company or plan cannot sustain high payouts. Or they change the deal so that they can keep more money than their distributors.

The result, I am pleased to say, is that the company crashes or the money dries up for people a few steps "down" the totem-pole line-of-sponsorship. Then we swoop in and whisper: "Only the guy at the top makes the *real* money."

That may be the fact, in a given case; but we quickly trick them into jumping--illogically--from the particular to the universal: "*All* these businesses are the same: the ordinary person gets in too late; only the top people make the money--so never try this kind of thing again. It's a scam."

Third, a few of these programs disregarded our advice: they had that awful quality, *integrity*. They produced superior products. They eschewed

17

debt; they funded expansion out of profits. They never changed their Bonus Plan except to give out *more* money.

The result: they have created a solid, legitimate, high-quality business opportunity, damn them! And worse for us in this case: the McDermotts and your targets are part of one of the best, perhaps *the* best of all these programs.

A clue for you: do not push Frank into a thorough investigation of these companies, programs, and approaches to multilevel. Much less should you encourage him to research the program he has joined. You would only deepen his commitment, once he perceives its excellence.

Your affectionate Mentor,
Shrewdtrap, S.C.
Department of Demonomics

From: Shrewdtrap@hellnet.edu
To: Warmwart@worldtrick.com
Subject: Questions about His Sponsor

My dear Warmwart:

So McDermott wants to help Frank, does he? I'm not surprised. That is the way this infernal system of theirs works: Frank will benefit by McDermott's ambitions and dreams for *his own* family.

Is there any way to convince Frank that he does not *need* McDermott's help?--that he, Frank, is smart enough to do it on his own ... that it would hurt his ego if he admitted that someone who does not have a Law Degree knows more about something than someone who does?

Tell me, when Frank and Jennifer talk about this, does Frank complain about McDermott's "interference"? Does he comment to her-- trying to impress her--that *he* knows how to talk to people, why, look at all the juries he has convinced over the years!

Let me know immediately. We may be able to leverage some failure into his efforts.

Your affectionate Mentor,
Shrewdtrap, S.C.
Department of Demonomics

———————

From: Shrewdtrap@hellnet.edu
To: Warmwart@worldtrick.com
Subject: How to Attack "The System"

My dear Warmwart:

Serphide, Scumslip, and Slantcreep have returned to Headquarters to get their M.T.A. at the Tempters College. They have filed a Report on their investigation of the program your targets have joined. I will summarize what they discovered.

Frank and Jennifer have joined an association of successful self-employed businessmen and women. It has a multi-faceted training/guidance program which they call, simply, "the System."

People who use the System are likely to succeed; those who do not are sure to fail.

Needless to say, you must direct your efforts toward keeping your targets out of the System. You can do this in a number of ways.

First, attack *the very idea* of a System. Remind Frank that the day he passed the Bar Exam he declared he hated schooling so much that he would "never take another class again in my life." Tell him that *he* is a smart fellow: why should *he* need to learn anything new?

Second, criticize *the way they do things*. If the meetings go long, suggest that it is unprofessional to drag things out. If a tape deals more with attitude than technique, whisper to Frank, "You don't need this stuff.

Your attitude is great already." As if an attorney couldn't improve his attitude!

Third, you say Frank and Jennifer are intellectual types. So criticize the *emotion* some speakers inject into their talks. *"You* don't need all this hoop-la, all this rah-rah stuff." A critical mind is not open. You want his mind to be hyper-critical and hyper-closed.

This is a complex topic. I will have more to say in a later communication. I may even come up there to review the situation myself. So stay on your toes.

> Your affectionate Mentor,
> Shrewdtrap, S.C.
> Department of Demonomics

From: Shrewdtrap@hellnet.edu
To: Warmwart@worldtrick.com
Subject: Don't Let Him Plant An Orchard

My dear Warmwart:

Don't you understand the stakes here? The tone of your last report hinted that you think your marvelous tempting talents are being wasted working on merely *one* couple.

But you are not really working on only *one* couple. Frank and Jennifer represent tens, hundreds, even thousands of people.

Learn a lesson from nature: one apple seed grows into an apple tree. Over its life it produces hundreds of apples. All of them have seeds. If these are planted and grow into, say, a hundred trees, now you have a whole orchard. Later, the seeds from this apple orchard could well produce dozens of orchards.

All from one apple seed.

Get it? McDermott planted the "seed" of a business idea in the minds of Frank and Jennifer. This business, unlike Frank's law practice, is *based on* "planting seeds."

Lawyers, doctors, dentists, plumbers, teachers, bus drivers-- *none of these* advances by teaching newcomers in law, medicine, dentistry, etc., how to be a better practitioner.

Quite the contrary: when the new Associate learns the tricks of the legal trade the firm *creates its own competition.* Once he thinks he's as good as the Senior Partners he wants to be paid as much as they. When he's not, he joins a competitor.

But this business of McDermott's is based on *duplication.* He will try to teach Frank and Jennifer everything he knows. To the extent you let them listen to him, they will think, act, and possibly achieve--McDermott's level of success. Or more.

The result: whole "orchards," as it were, of other people duplicating them. This is why you must kill the seed before it grows into a tree. So get back to work and stop complaining!

Your affectionate Mentor,
Shrewdtrap, S.C.
Department of Demonomics

From: Shrewdtrap@hellnet.edu
To: Warmwart@worldtrick.com
Subject: The Hidden Danger of Pictures

My dear Warmwart:

With a certain pompous sarcasm, you note that Frank and Jennifer have *put pictures on their refrigerator.* She has a simple photo of their little family at a beach, with the words, "Time to Play Together!" written on it. And he has a full-color ad for a Nautilus machine.

You make light of this; indeed, you think it is silly. You seem not to grasp *why* they did this.

First, the idea probably was McDermott's. You may assume that whatever he suggests has merit, from his perspective. Thus you should oppose it. Did you whisper to your targets, "Better not put pictures up, of things you want--because if you don't get them, you will be even more disappointed"?

No, you didn't, because you have such a limited grasp of human psychology. I sometimes think everything I tell you goes in one ear and out the other!

So I will explain, yet again... The humans need to have motivation. They get it from a "dream" or a vision: something they don't have that they really want. The more they remind themselves of what they want, the more they are moved to *do* something to get it.

There are "success motivation systems," Warmwart, which preach these principles but give the listener no way to *practice* the preachments. The audience leaves all pumped up by the seminar speaker--but by Monday morning they are back in the old rut. Only the speaker gets the money--his fee.

Our targets are in a practical program. Everything abstract they learn has a concrete application. This is very bad, for it minimizes the frustration factor.

Don't you realize why Frank and Jennifer put up those pictures: every time Frank opens the refrigerator door, to get the makings of another fattening sandwich, he sees the exercise equipment he *wants* for a home gym in the wing on his house he *wants* to add. Every time she is cooking, she sees the family "with time to be together," as she keeps mumbling to herself.

Whatever keeps their Dream before their eyes will harm their prospects of failure. Even pictures on a refrigerator. Especially there.

Your affectionate Mentor,
Shrewdtrap, S.C.
Department of Demonomics

From: Shrewdtrap@hellnet.edu
To: Warmwart@worldtrick.com
Subject: The Uses of Short-term Success

My dear Warmwart:

Slinkruse and Sneertwist are quite skilled at orchestrating automobile accidents. At my request, the Department of Social Mayhem has loaned them to us at Demonomics.

I am planning to contrive a distraction: send Slinkruse and Sneertwist up there to arrange some accidents. Steer the victims toward the firm where Frank does litigation. They will motivate these victims to engage his services.

There is nothing like loading a trial attorney's plate with a pile of personal injury cases to whet his greedy appetite and to get him so busy that all his energy is absorbed in suing people.

Give him short-term success, I say, so that his mind is pulled away from thinking about long-term financial security. Not to mention keeping him out of the gym as his waistline expands.

In the past, you have questioned the wisdom of helping a human being to achieve *any* success. But the End justifies the Means, Warmwart! Anyway, the Means, here, is *pseudo* success.

Your affectionate Mentor,
Shrewdtrap, S.C.
Department of Demonomics

From: Shrewdtrap@hellnet.edu
To: Warmwart@worldtrick.com
Subject: Keep His List Short

My dear Warmwart:

There is a step toward success in this program that, if you are clever, might trip Frank and Jennifer up. They need to build a List of people to whom to show the program.

One would think that if a person's sponsor asked them to build a List, the person would do it. After all, the sponsor wants them to succeed and surely would not waste their time with make work.

But in studying people in this business, we have noted that many do not really do a good job of List-building. I'll tell you why; then you can motivate Frank to make the same mistakes.

First, a man will say, "I don't know anybody." This is not true, of course: if you offered him $100.00 for each name plus phone number he could come up with, he would quickly relieve you of $10,000.00. A person with a poor self-image uses this excuse.

Second, he might say, "I have all the names in my head." This is untrue, too: humans can remember roughly five names at a time. After that, they need to write them down, to make room in their heads for the next five. A person who is lazy uses this excuse.

Third, often a new person will pre-qualify and reject names, not by asking them whether they keep their options open re more time or money, but by telling themselves, "He's doing o.k." or "He's too busy." A person who is intimidated by another's prestige uses this excuse.

I assume Frank will not fool himself with the first excuse. He may swallow the second: if he writes down only a few names, you may be able to exclude some people from his list, e.g., the mailman, the manager at the gas station, even the paralegal in his firm.

Oddly enough, despite his success as a lawyer, in the case of physicians and other attorney acquaintances, the third excuse may prevent Frank from listing them. Suggest it wherever you can.

In a couple years, if he is still in this awful business, it will be a blow to his morale to run into some doctor he knew but did not approach--who by then is part of someone else's group!

Your affectionate Mentor,
Shrewdtrap, S.C.
Department of Demonomics

From: Shrewdtrap@hellnet.edu
To: Warmwart@worldtrick.com
Subject: Danger! McDermott's Wife

Warmwart! I should scald you in brimstone myself! Why didn't you brief me about *all* soldiers in the war??!! You did not tell me about McDermott's *wife*, Maryann, until now.

It seems she is a formidable adversary: you say she is smart, pretty, organized, pleasant, determined, and on and on, *ad nauseam*. To hear you describe her, she has every single bad quality we could imagine. A veritable monster of virtue.

No wonder you did not inform me about her: you cannot possibly think of a way to deal with her in this fight, so, like a human who avoids facing a painful task by doing something else, you spent your time on other matters.

Well, for us to avoid reality will not bring humans down here or bring them financial failure up there. *We* must be clear-eyed realists; *they* are the ones we must teach to be blind romantics.

Now you say that Jennifer has taken a shine to this likeable Maryann and is willing to listen to her as a new friend.

This is a major setback. It means that Jennifer will absorb, almost by osmosis, all of Maryann's bad qualities. A woman like this probably has a great relationship with her husband. Thus, because she will be a role model, the chances of causing a rift between Frank and Jennifer will drop.

The only course now is to keep the four of them apart; cook up distractions so Jennifer cannot attend meetings with Maryann. If you have to, get their nanny Maria sick so Jennifer has to stay home. Do *anything* to limit Maryann's influence!

Your affectionate Mentor,
Shrewdtrap, S.C.
Department of Demonomics

From: Shrewdtrap@hellnet.edu
To: Warmwart@worldtrick.com
Subject: Keep Him Arguing

My dear Warmwart:

There are advantages and disadvantages in dealing with an attorney as your target.

Attorneys love to argue. You inform me Frank is a successful attorney. I would think that this success is due, at least in part, to his skill in debate: he wins lots of arguments.

The humans have sayings, "A man convinced against his will is of the same opinion still," and "Win an argument, lose a friend."

When he offers this business program to prospects, he will be tempted--by *you*, Warmwart!, as well as his past mental habits--to argue them into it. This is good. Every argument won will be a prospect lost.

To increase the odds of early failure, steer toward him two kinds of prospects who will be immune to his argument. Indeed, they will be immune to the common sense that is in the business program he has joined.

First, tell him that "people who *really need* the money" are the ones most likely to join. Steer him toward people far *below* his level of ambition; for example, the 22-year-old who handles the mail in his firm will not be able to imagine himself with an extra $3,000.00 to $5,000.00 per month, *and part-time* at that!

Remember, the average American cannot visualize income more than 20% higher than it is now. Keep Frank talking with below average people.

Second, go to the opposite extreme: aim him at the most high-powered professionals he knows; start with the Senior Partners in his firm. Though probably they are just as "time-bankrupt" as Frank is, they may not have a wife like Jennifer who reminds them of it.

But--this is important--do *not* pick people at random: evaluate them *before* you let them discuss time and money. The last thing you want is another doctor or lawyer sick of long hours at the office!

Select narrow-minded, negative, hypercritical types. These people never accept a good idea from anyone but the person they see in a mirror.

Frank will try to argue them into joining. They may laugh at him. Since attorneys usually take themselves very seriously, that laughter may blow him right out.

Your affectionate Mentor,
Shrewdtrap, S.C.
Department of Demonomics

My dear Warmwart:

Time may be his Achilles heel after all. You say McDermott attends evening "opportunity meetings" twice a month at a hotel. He invites Frank to join him and bring a prospect. McDermott offers to pre-qualify the prospect by means of a ten-minute overview a few days prior to the meeting.

This may be an "opportunity" for *us*, as well: do all you can to discourage any prospect from attending. Frank will either (a) also not go, or (b) attend but with misgivings, since two or three hours will slip by for, you must tell him, nothing.

Either way, we win: if he stays away, he misses association with McDermott, the chance to meet others with the same mindset, and learning from a *different* presentation. If he does attend, his "wasted time" will begin to grind on him. Negative thoughts in humans are good, Warmwart. Always cultivate them.

During the meeting, whisk yourself over to Frank's house, and whisper to Jennifer that Frank is spending too much time away from her, at these stupid meetings.

She may not "buy" this ploy immediately, but doubt about the truth comes before conviction about a lie. So start seeding doubts. In due time they may blossom into belief in lies.

> Your affectionate Mentor,
> Shrewdtrap, S.C.
> Department of Demonomics

From: Shrewdtrap@hellnet.edu
To: Warmwart@worldtrick.com
Subject: The Principle of Delayed Gratification

My dear Warmwart:

So you visited Jennifer while Frank was at the meeting. And what did you discover?

You found out that Maryann McDermott had beaten you to the punch! A few days ago, she invited Jennifer to her house where the latter "happened" to come across a sign on McDermotts' refrigerator:

"I will do things today that others will not do, so that tomorrow I can enjoy things others will not have."

As disgusting an expression of the Principle of Delayed Gratification as I have ever read! This horrible maxim runs counter to all our teaching. We want them to pursue instant gratification, not to sacrifice for future benefit.

Worse still, it seems Maryann had remarked, quite in passing, I'm sure, that she applies that maxim to every inconvenience, even her husband's time away at a meeting instead of being home with her.

She drove the point home by joking, "I'd rather be a 'business meeting widow' temporarily than a 'Monday Night Football widow' permanently." That struck a chord with Jennifer, since Frank is a football fanatic. Or he *was*, until you let the McDermotts warp his thinking.

Warmwart, a successful Tempter must be proactive. Begin to anticipate what tricks McDermott and wife will pull. For hell's sake, Warmwart, who's Tempter here, you or them?

> Your affectionate Mentor,
> Shrewdtrap, S.C.
> Department of Demonomics

From: Shrewdtrap@hellnet.edu
To: Warmwart@worldtrick.com
Subject: The Value of Tapes

My dear Warmwart:

According to Slantcreep, they have hundreds of tapes. McDermott calls them "tools." While you stood idly by, pondering your next move, he gave--*gave*, not *sold*--Frank six or eight tapes.

I notice he also preempted any procrastination tactic you might employ: he told Frank, "I need these back by the end of the week, to loan to someone else. But you can easily go through them in the car on the way to the office."

So he inserted a time limit. And doubtless Frank, being an attorney used to deadlines, will comply. Look what you've allowed to happen!

McDermott has transferred the training to six other people, some of whom Frank will like. It will be easy for Frank to learn from them, and yet keep his independence: he can turn the tape off when all those red brake lights pop up ahead or he is just tired of listening.

Worse still, Frank can turn the damned things back *on* whenever he wants. If an especially good phrase strikes him, he can rewind and listen again. Humans need to hear something 21 times before it really sinks in.

Then too, because that blasted Maryann McDermott mentioned to Jennifer that she, Maryann, listens to the same tapes that Steve does, so they are "both on the same page," Frank and Jennifer will do the same. No more exchanges about daily problems.

Finally, Frank now has the idea that *he* should get on Tape of the Month, Tape of the Week, Tape of the Day, Tape of the Hour, or whatever schedule they have, so that he in turn can loan tapes to the people he sponsors. See how the thing snowballs??!!

Your affectionate Mentor,
Shrewdtrap, S.C.
Department of Demonomics

31

From: Shrewdtrap@hellnet.edu
To: Warmwart@worldtrick.com
Subject: How Not to Create a Lioness

My dear Warmwart:

How could you not pay attention to their three-year-old son Tommy?!! Don't you know that children blurt things out without thinking? It should be easy to coach a child what to say, and what *not* to say!!

Instead, right before your eyes, when Maria was leaving for the night, little Tommy said to Maria, "Bye-bye, Mommy." *Mommy!!?* And you let him say this *right in front of Jennifer!*

Her reaction was predictable. She maintained her composure, wished Maria a friendly goodbye, picked up Tommy and explained to him that *she, Jennifer,* is the Mommy and that Maria is only a helper--and she resolved to quit her job immediately.

Warmwart, when a normal human mother sees she is about to lose her child, whether physically to an accident or psychologically through transfer of affection [as here], she turns into a lioness protecting her cub.

Now our task is much harder. Now there is no point in tempting Jennifer away from this business. Now she has an *emotional* commitment.

I sometimes think the Tempters College should offer more courses in human psychology. I'd send you back for a refresher, in light of this incident, except that we are underfiended in your sector and your absence would leave McDermott and his wife in full control of the battle. Better to have an unskilled tempter shadowing them than no one. Now go redeem yourself by working on Frank.

Your affectionate Mentor,
Shrewdtrap, S.C.
Department of Demonomics

P.S.: Your incompetence in this incident is being recorded in your file.

---

* Author's note: the names are changed, but this is otherwise a true story. It happened to a client of mine.

From: Shrewdtrap@hellnet.edu
To: Warmwart@worldtrick.com
Subject: The Internet Business Tidal Wave

My dear Warmwart:

The Slantcreep Report reminded me that this Business has moved aggressively onto the Internet.

I worked for a time in the Department of Cultural Depravity, Pornography Division; so I grasp the Internet's importance. Properly manipulated, it can corrupt millions of people. Or, more accurately, help them corrupt themselves.

But it also has potential for genuine good. Slantcreep's Report warns that if we are not careful, many ordinary people will start shoe-string businesses and ride the E-Commerce wave to extraordinary prosperity.

Of course, some of them will charge out and do it themselves, rather than with a team of other businessmen and women. They will do all the work alone: advertise, handle orders, stock inventory, deal with returns, man phone banks for complaints...

All this can wear them out, especially if they have limited time for their new business. We always teach them to do everything on their own-- "this way you get to keep all the profits"--and then maneuver them into failure.

I regret that this business of McDermott's has finessed these problems for the individual business owners associated with it.

They do not spend any money advertising: it is done word-of-mouth, by each person in their network.

They do not stock inventory, except enough for their own needs and perhaps one extra of the most popular items, to show to potential customers.

They do not deal with returns or telephone complaints: as with inventory, there is a servicing corporation that does this "grunt work."

The Internet dimension complicates our task: we might have steeled Frank against an ordinary networking business, on the grounds that it would take him too much time selling products to customers. But E-Commerce goes on 24 hours a day.

No longer. By now, Frank realizes he is on a tidal wave, if only he will ride it. So do not deny the wave exists; rather, try to knock him off it ... or make it so choppy that he gets sick of it.

Your affectionate Mentor,
Shrewdtrap, S.C.
Department of Demonomics

From: Shrewdtrap@hellnet.edu
To: Warmwart@worldtrick.com
Subject: A Numbers Game

My Dear Warmwart:

You say that McDermott and Frank had a home meeting, they invited twenty people "to hear an expert on Internet business explain how to develop a strong second income using E-Commerce," fifteen showed up, and a dozen "got in." And you think this is a disaster.

Indeed, it would have been better if nobody had got in. But the fact many did does not win the war for them.

You seem not to understand that we can profit when the market goes up and we can profit when the market goes down: it is possible to turn his apparent success into the basis for failure. But you will have to move much faster.

The twelve newcomers need the "the System" as badly as Frank does. So hover around the least committed new people and repeat the temptations I explained in past E-mails. You should be able to lure at least four of them into the Black Hole of Forgetfulness.

As soon as pressures of life, obstacles, doubts, negative comments interfere, many people simply forget that they saw a way to obtain their Dreams.

Now, when four or five people *do nothing*--do not show up for a training meeting, do not build a List, do not listen to a tape, do not even answer phone calls--this should shake Frank up. Tell him it's like losing a case in court: he just lost four or five cases!

That is a lie; there is no analogy. In court, he appeals to juries whose decision does not affect their own lives and he has days and days to introduce evidence and make arguments. Here, the prospects are personally affected by their decisions, which we can talk them into making without sufficient information.

So do not let your morale flag. This is a long-term project.

The game is not over until it's over.

> Your affectionate Mentor,
> Shrewdtrap, S.C.
> Department of Demonomics

From: Shrewdtrap@hellnet.edu
To: Warmwart@worldtrick.com
Subject: Books versus Television

My dear Warmwart:

You mention that their training System includes the strong recommendation that they read books. You laugh, since we have Americans wasting gobs of time watching television. And for once you make an astute comment: "When a person watches television, he watches *someone else* succeed."

Yes, he can watch Tiger Woods sink a putt, or Dan Rather read the news, or a new game show where someone wins a million dollars. In each case he sits there mesmerized by the tube, waistline expanding, wallet shrinking, *spectator to someone else's success.*

Americans are now so hooked on TV that our Department of Statistics uses a simple, but very accurate, prediction formula:

"A human achieves financial success in inverse proportion to the number of hours he spends in front of the TV set."

But that is an aside. I mention it only because there is a time conflict for the TV addict who, now that he is in this business, hears he should read a self-improvement book every day. And Frank loves to watch football.

The easiest solution for him would simply be to *turn the TV set off!* But that he will not do, unless he knows *why.*

Notice that these two elements, (1) turning it off, and (2) the reason/motive to do so, symbolize their entire business: it has its technical side, the "How"; and its motivational side, the "Why."

If a person knows "Why," he will figure out "How." So confuse Frank and Jennifer on why they should read these books.

To stimulate your thought processes, in your next communication *you* tell me why you think their System includes reading books.

Your affectionate Mentor,
Shrewdtrap, S.C.
Department of Demonomics

From: Shrewdtrap@hellnet.edu
To: Warmwart@worldtrick.com
Subject: The Value of Negative Words

My dear Warmwart:

Long ago our research on human psychology made it clear that humans do not like to change. Keep that in mind as you work on these new people in Frank and Jennifer's group.

In their business, they need to cultivate positive habits, thinking positive, speaking positive.

If a person has habituated himself to speaking negative, or looking for negative, he has to overcome this thought process. He has to change it.

Engineers tend to be negative: they want things to be very precise and are critical when they are not. Attorneys tend to be negative: they are trained to find flaws in arguments, loopholes in contracts. Scientists such as doctors tend to the same: they look for debility, problems, disease.

You want to urge this kind of person, should he join this business, to maintain his negative mindset. Get him to *speak* the negative thoughts you seed into his mind. I'll give a few examples:

- "This takes too much time..."
- "This is not your cup of tea..."
- "Your personality is not cut out for this..."
- "That speaker does not really believe what he's saying..."
- "The products cost too much..."
- "The website is not as user-friendly as others..."
- "If your wife won't help you, you can't do it on your own..."

Notice the prominence of *not* and *can't...*? For humans, *speaking* difficulty creates *more* difficulty. They start *to think* difficulty.

It is interesting that none of these statements is usually true; but what is objectively true does not matter. What they think is true is all that counts.

When they repeat what they think cannot do, they deepen their belief that they cannot. Since they are built to achieve that which they first think, when they think failure they soon achieve failure.

Remember, whatever the mind of man cannot conceive, or cannot believe, the man cannot achieve. Perhaps not every time, for now and then a human can force himself to try even though he believes he will fail. But most of the time using negative words and entertaining negative thoughts lead to negative results.

I think the reason is that winning in life is like winning in an athletic contest: the runner who doubts he can beat the others has in effect tied weights to his belt. His doubts slow him down. So he does not beat the others. Self-fulfilling prophecy.

Every negative word plants a weed in the garden of his mind. Get those weeds growing!

> Your affectionate Mentor,
> Shrewdtrap, S.C.
> Department of Demonomics

From: Shrewdtrap@hellnet.edu
To: Warmwart@worldtrick.com
Subject: The Harm from Reading

My dear Warmwart:

Watch out for an end run by that miserable Maryann! You have summarized some of her chats with Jennifer. You note, apparently without appreciating its importance, Maryann's "chance" remark that she and Steve improved their skill with people by reading *How to Win Friends and Influence People*.

I was afraid of this. As long as Frank stewed in his own discontents, his natural tendency to blow up at stupidity would drive out of his business most of the people he brought in. Didn't you study our Intelligence Report on him? Let me refresh your recollection...

A year ago, just for the fun of it, Frank picked verbal fights with people wearing a political button urging a vote for the other party's candidate. And his sarcastic courtroom cross-examination was legendary among his peers. He not only put the knife in; he enjoyed twisting it.

Now he enters a business where relationships with other people are central to success. No longer can he wear his likes and dislikes on his sleeve. Nor can he be so blunt. No longer can he feed his ego with rapier verbal thrusts that cut up friend and foe alike, leaving many of them deeply wounded.

And that is where the reading comes in. You were not able to imagine any good reasons why their book program is important; perhaps *you* should read Dale Carnegie, too. Then you would understand: the books help them improve their attitude, their personality, their style with others.

Beyond that, the books inspire with the stories of people overcoming obstacles, teach persistence, dilute self-pity, build confidence. For an investment of a mere 15-30 minutes a day, a person like Frank can learn how to win--not terrorize--and influence--not browbeat--people.

The next time McDermott makes a suggestion to either Frank or Jennifer, for hell's sake, treat it as a rapier thrust at *you!*

> Your affectionate Mentor,
> Shrewdtrap, S.C.
> Department of Demonomics

From: Shrewdtrap@hellnet.edu
To: Warmwart@worldtrick.com
Subject: The Merits of Multiple Outlets

My dear Warmwart:

Here is an economic insight. Should you see McDermott starting to explain it to Frank's group, do anything you can to interrupt. The topic is *Multiple Outlets*.

In America in the latter 20th Century, a system of "franchising" emerged. Ray Kroc developed McDonalds restaurants; Tom Monahan developed Dominos Pizza. There sprang up many other associations of franchised businesses which duplicated an original successful model.

The problem for most *individuals* is that they spend virtually all their waking hours chasing money, *because they rely solely on their own time.* They gain no benefit from other people's time. This is true of the truck driver, the teacher, the corporate manager--and your target, Frank the Attorney.

Every human has only 24 hours in a day. Unlike us, they must sleep and eat. This uses up eight to ten hours. When they add 10 to 12 hours on a job, they are almost out of time. We push them over the edge by encouraging round-trip automobile commuting for another hour or two. These days our Road Rage Division is highly productive.

Did you do the math? Add ten plus twelve plus one. Even if everything goes well, husband and wife end up with scarcely any time to play with their children and share time with each other. When do they exercise? When go to the doctor and dentist?

When our Road Rage Division throws in a good Rush Hour accident, ten thousand parents miss their boys' soccer games or arrive an hour late at the Day Care Center to pick up their crying two-year-old.

They complain that they have no time to raise their kids, to jog, to go to the gym, to see each other. But rarely do they get to the heart of the problem: *when people rely solely on their own time to make money, they will always run out of time.* And rarely do they make enough money.

This is where "multiple outlets" come in. Until a system of "private franchising" emerged in the 1960's, the ordinary *individual* human could not multiply his time through "franchises" that would market the same kind of product or service at a different time and in a different location.

Oh yes, law firms sometimes have branch offices. Film stars market films through multiple movie theaters. Computer companies market their product through multiple stores. No longer do they make all their money in one place; now they make some money in many places.

But the average *individual* remained stuck in the one-job/24-hour rut that took all his time and paid little money--until private franchising came along.

But now that is all changed. McDermott and Frank can "multiply themselves" through the work of others *whom they help.*

Actually, using E-Commerce as a new way to order through the computer, they can multiply themselves through every computer in the land.

So, unless you display more brains than you have so far, they will break out of the rut entirely by helping these others--their "front line"--help others in turn.

Over 30 human years ago, a wealthy man named J. Paul Getty remarked, "I would rather have 1% of the labor of each of 100 men than 100% of the labor of only one man." That is true whether the one man is an employee or is oneself.

Can you see the advantages of such an approach? First, if the "one man" gets sick, no money is made. But if one of the 100 get sick, the person still earns 99%.

Second, if a snowstorm, a traffic jam, or a medical emergency in the family prevents the one man from getting to work at all, he makes no money that day. But those problems never arise for *all hundred* at one time. Not even for ten of them.

Third, marketplace competition can drive the sole proprietor out of business. Look at how Wal-Mart decimated the population of country stores in the small towns it entered. Where were all the "Mom and Pop" motels, once Holiday Inn and a dozen clones of their system materialized across the street?

Fourth, when the "one man" retires, he stops earning income. But if he has left behind him an association of "many men" [and women] who continue working, producing, marketing, making money themselves--then he will continue to earn a small percentage of the value of their work. He stops but his income does not.

This is the essence of a well-funded Retirement: to have money continue to come in, permanently, repetitively, even after one discontinues the work that earned the money.

In a job, one might be able to save enough, and invest prudently enough, to achieve this result after forty years. But in this business of McDermott and Frank, one can achieve this result in two to five years. Maybe less.

They do *not* have a job on the side. Their business is not a second job. They are building a team of people each of whom will, if they are smart, build his or her own team in turn. And they will be paid a small percent of the value of the work of each person they help to succeed.

So keep their new people ignorant of this truth. Ignorance for the mind is what the "rut" is for their daily time-bankrupt schedules.

Your affectionate Mentor,
Shrewdtrap, S.C.
Department of Demonomics

From: Shrewdtrap@hellnet.edu
To: Warmwart@worldtrick.com
Subject: Useful Lies

My dear Warmwart:

Lies ... fallacies ... shallow thinking ... unexamined arguments ... prejudices ... half-truths ... these and other mental twists and turns are our stock in trade.

These techniques have produced great progress in the 20th Century confusing human thinking. Quite a few of them never wonder whether what they believe is *true*. Many repeat other people's ignorant opinions without ever checking them out.

Lies can work here too. Keep in mind what lies or half-truths you can suggest to these new people that McDermott and Frank sponsored into Frank's group. I will give a rejoinder in brackets, so you can prepare to rebut McDermott's likely answer.

"This looks like a pyramid." [Answer: "I think I understand how you feel. I felt the same way, until someone pointed out that every organization is shaped like a pyramid, from Exxon and IBM to colleges and churches and the government."]

"I don't want to *use* my friends." ["Neither would I. But when we show your friends how to buy products at discount and, if they want, how to earn some good extra income, that's *helping*, not using, them."]

"I like to shop at the stores." ["Could you change the place you buy things, if buying from your *own* store, and teaching others to do the same, would get you out of debt and free up enough time that you could go to the gym three times a week?"]

"We're doing o.k." ["That's great. I thought I was, too, until I realized that I spent more time in rush hour every day than with my kids. I decided that along with money, this business could give me more time for my family."]

Now, here's a simple test for you: pretend you are the prospect; come up with a good self-deceptive reply to McDermott.

Your affectionate Mentor,
Shrewdtrap, S.C.
Department of Demonomics

From: Shrewdtrap@hellnet.edu
To: Warmwart@worldtrick.com
Subject: Don't Let Them Buy From Themselves

My dear Warmwart:

A few E-mails ago, I sent Slinkruse up to the United States to spy on people in this business. He informs me that new marketing associates are expected to shop for their needs from their "own" suppliers.

They are urged to buy from their own store, give the profit back to their own business rather than to a competitor, create volume. McDermott will say to Frank, "If you were a Cadillac salesman, you wouldn't drive a Lincoln."

This makes sense. It will be hard for you to convince them--intellectually--that it does not matter whether they "buy from their own store," through a toll-free phone number or by clicking onto an Internet website, rather than go to Safeway, Sears, or Seven-Eleven.

Yet if they fail to make this transition, they will have no credibility with others. So it is important, if you can, to discourage them from doing it. Remember the process of Duplication: whatever they do--or fail to do--their "downline" will duplicate.

So create belief that changing their shopping habits is too inconvenient. You may not be able to keep them from changing their *minds;* so you must try to inhibit them from changing their *habits.*

Humans are creatures of habit, which for them is what instincts are for animals. They develop habits through voluntary repetition. They can develop *good* habits: e.g., brushing their teeth after meals; or--with our help--*bad* habits: e.g., driving too fast, drinking too much alcohol.

Some habits are neutral, such as where they shop. They're *used to* Safeway and 7-11. They're used to paying *someone else* for their products--to being a *customer* of someone else rather than an *entrepreneur* in a business where they buy from themselves.

Tell Jennifer she *likes* what she gets from Safeway. Tell her it's too much trouble to make a list of what she might run out of before she does, and then get it from her own business. Tell her that she can start doing that *later*.

Have you noticed that humans who measure the *value* of a course of action in terms of "like," "trouble" [i.e., convenience], and "later" are never successful?

> Your affectionate Mentor,
> Shrewdtrap, S.C.
> Department of Demonomics

From: Shrewdtrap@hellnet.edu
To: Warmwart@worldtrick.com
Subject: Mental Detours at Their Weekend Conference

My dear Warmwart:

There are different ways you can deflect the remaining eight people in Frank's--i.e., McDermott and Frank's--new group from success.

You say they have a weekend Business Conference coming up soon. Naturally McDermott and Frank and their wives want these new people to attend. They will "see the big picture." They will absorb plenty of good teaching. They will even--damn them!--have *fun*.

Your first tactic is standard: tell them it costs too much, it is too far away, they're tired on the weekend and need to sleep at home, the yard needs mowing, the cat is sick--tell them anything to keep them away.

If McDermott and his horrible wife Maryann, along with Frank and Jennifer [who, despite your supposed brilliance, are now deeply involved in "the System"], rebut these objections and these folks do show up at the Conference, then you go to Step Two.

Which is to check out the speakers in advance. Figure out which ones might offend or irritate these new people. After all, personality and style may be superficial compared to the long-term substance of this business, but many people let the superficial supplant the substantive.

If a speaker has an annoying mannerism, point it out. If the speaker digresses into politics for a minute, blow that out of proportion as if it took up the whole weekend. If a female speaker is too pretty, promote envy in female listeners.

Mannerisms, political comments, beauty--all totally beside the point-- are useful distractions from the essentials.

Remember, Warmwart, all mental detours will slow their progress along the main highway. If you play your cards right, you can detour them into a Dead End.

> Your affectionate Mentor,
> Shrewdtrap, S.C.
> Department of Demonomics

From: Shrewdtrap@hellnet.edu
To: Warmwart@worldtrick.com
Subject: "Mixed Results" at the Conference

My dear Warmwart:

So the weekend Conference had "mixed results," did it? Let me analyze that.

On the good side, the fluid schedule irritated one of the eight, a crotchety attorney; he thought it was "unprofessional." Never occurred to him, did it, that not a few Judges come back to Court long after their lunch break should be finished.

This fellow allows himself to be distracted by trivia. He is probably looking for an excuse to bow out. As long as you can keep him from McDermott and Frank's bad influence, he will quit.

Another good development: one of the female speakers droned on and on about her luxuries; this commentary bothered a couple in the group, whose interest in this program is not a new Jaguar or two fur coats, but simply paying two teenagers' imminent college tuition.

Keep their minds on someone else's cars and coats; their minds off the fact that if Mr. and Mrs. X can *afford* a Jaguar and furs, *a fortiori* they can afford college tuition--and that the issue is *not* how people at the podium *spend* their money but how they *earned* it.

To turn to the bad side. I fear it is worse than you let on. First, you admit that that monstrous angel Maryann struck up friendships with the wives that were there. She offered to help them any time.

Worse still, at least four men in the new group noticed that the Conference attracted over three thousand sharp people ... the meeting drew people of all ages and races ... and worst of all, they heard persuasive speakers from their own professions.

And throughout this sickening display of growing enthusiasm, you could only whisper to the physician in the new group, regarding another physician about give a talk, that "He couldn't be much of a doctor if he has to do *this* on the side"!

47

What a lame comment, Warmwart! Didn't you first check out the speaker's resume? The man graduated from a leading medical school and is a heart surgeon; as a matter of fact, he used to be Chief of Cardiology at the finest university hospital in the Midwest.

Before you sneak into the next weekend Conference, make a quick trip back here to Headquarters first. Bring the resumes of all the likely speakers. *I* will figure out a way to neutralize them.

> Your affectionate Mentor,
> Shrewdtrap, S.C.
> Department of Demonomics

From: Shrewdtrap@hellnet.edu
To: Warmwart@worldtrick.com
Subject: Association

My dear Warmwart:

Association. We may win or lose the war on the battlefield of association.

Unlike our personalities and character, beautifully formed in permanent self-possession, human beings can grow and change and improve their psychology, attitudes, and habits.

So we have had to scrutinize them carefully, over many eons, to determine what outside influences lead them to make small choices which, over years, add up to big changes.

Fortunately for tempters like you, the wisdom of the ages is available to you in my brilliance. Thus you don't have to figure these things out yourself. You probably couldn't.

The outside influences boil down to one element: association with other human beings. As a general rule, with so few exceptions that they are statistically irrelevant, humans become like the books they read and the people they associate with.

I should add that this means *interactive* association and, quite often, associating with others *in a shared purpose*. Obviously, when a person attends a movie, he does not become like the anonymous strangers sitting around him. His contacts with them are too meaningless, trivial, and momentary.

But to some extent, he does take on the attitudes of--become like--the character on the screen he most approves of or identifies with. If a teenage gang leader is the film's protagonist, many teenagers in the audience will leave feeling that that lifestyle is "pretty cool."

If a woman spends many hours absorbed in romance novels, she will take on much of the mentality of the romantic heroine. So too will the young male stud who immerses himself in sex magazines come to approve the soft-core pornography these glorify.

I mention the evil side of association, because that is the side of the street we work. Unfortunately for us, the rules of human psychology can be the basis for inculcating habits and attitudes that are really good for them. For example, this regrettable result often occurs through the efforts of a high school or college coach with the kids on his team.

Coming to the point: when we look at how to corrupt a business based on Duplication, we must keep in mind that the best way the humans can learn *what* to duplicate and *what attitude* to cultivate is to *get around others who already are doing the task right.*

That is another way of saying: association. When they read the books their leaders recommend, they associate mentally, on their own time and at their own convenience, with writers or characters in the story, who overcame obstacles, improved themselves, helped others, showed character, etc.

When they attend a meeting, whether at a home or a hotel, they get around many others who are in the same self-improvement quest. They also imbibe the technical teaching and subjective attitudes of the speaker,

49

a person who is "doing the task right," in much the same way as a sponge absorbs water.

So Warmwart, from now on you must consider this point a continuous working maxim. Do all you can to convince Frank and Jennifer and the many people who now have joined their group, that there's just too much trouble in driving all those miles to get to that meeting.

> Your affectionate Mentor,
> Shrewdtrap, S.C.
> Department of Demonomics

From: Shrewdtrap@hellnet.edu
To: Warmwart@worldtrick.com
Subject: The Use of Fallacies

My dear Warmwart:

Your last missive showed the proper humility. I realize that it is feigned, since *we* cannot understand, much less practice, humility. But you were so clever in disguising what I know is really your resentment at *my* superior powers of analysis, that I almost believed you.

This improvement in your style suggests that my excellent advice must be sinking, however slowly, into your thick head. Perhaps the time I spend slaving over a hot keyboard is not wasted after all.

So you asked me, obsequiously, what to do about that doctor in Frank and McDermott's growing group.

Slantcreep tells me he attended the same conference as McDermott and your other targets. Slantcreep's charge was a physician who is so fed up with malpractice insurance premiums, trial lawyers, HMOs and Blue Cross reductions-in-fee that he is looking for a side business to make up for all the money being drained away.

That doctor and Frank chanced to strike up a conversation before the Saturday session began. Slantcreep then reminded his target that Frank is a trial lawyer. He added, "You don't want to get in bed with *them*, do you?" Why don't you try the same ploy with your man?

Keep in mind, however, that this assertion, as an appeal to prejudice, is based on an improper mental jump from a particular to a universal: "Some people in group X or with quality Y are bad, *therefore* everyone, *all* people in group X or having Y are bad." This does not follow logically.

It may occur to that doctor that not all trial lawyers are rapacious sharks. As a matter of fact, not all of them are plaintiffs' attorneys. There are as many trial lawyers who defend doctors against real or trumped-up medical malpractice claims as attack them.

But human beings are not primarily logical. They are primarily emotional. So this fallacy might work. But even if it does not, the longer you keep them muddled with fallacies, the later it will be that they break out of their mental paralysis and *do* something.

Little lies are like mosquitoes buzzing their heads as they walk in the woods: though brushed off easily, they do distract. If you can't think of a good big lie, at least come up with a bad little one. Half a lie is better than none.

Your affectionate Mentor,
Shrewdtrap, S.C.
Department of Demonomics

51

From: Shrewdtrap@hellnet.edu
To: Warmwart@worldtrick.com
Subject: "Burn the Ships!"

My dear Warmwart:

You say Frank goes around mumbling, "Burn the Ships!" You wonder whether this is code, a prayer, or a mantra.

The answer is that it is one more form of effective self-motivation that you have allowed Frank to absorb from McDermott or from some tape.

Here's the background: legend has it that when Julius Caesar was the greatest Roman general, he first conquered Gaul, which is now called France. Then he took a few companies across the Channel to attack the Celts, who controlled what is now called England.

He and his warriors captured a beachhead and sent patrols out to scout the enemy. They returned to warn that the Celts outnumbered Caesar's Romans by a large number. Prudence would dictate returning to France. Instead, Caesar ordered, "Burn the ships!" They did.

Since you've observed humans for eons now, you will readily guess what happened: the Roman soldiers, having no way to retreat, fought ferociously. They had no option but to win. Despite the odds, they did.

Because at the time this battle occurred I was in the Far East, I did not personally observe Caesar as he spoke his bold ultimatum. Nor have I bothered to locate some fiend who was there as a witness. So I cannot affirm that my account is absolutely accurate.

But for our purposes, we must assume that it is. Beyond that, the important point is that Frank believes it is. And the main point is: he is using this--call it a mantra, if you will--to strengthen his motivation.

Every time his stress at work or you yourself tempt him to postpone today's business effort until tomorrow, he will repeat this phrase and strengthen his resolve. His words remind him of the Roman soldiers' courage.

52

They also deepen his commitment to make this business work. The phrase is shorthand for saying, "I have no option but to succeed." He is reminding himself that the Channel's cold waters lie behind; conquest by the enemy--lack of time controlling his life--lies ahead. Unless of course, he wins.

Pay closer attention, Warmwart, to repetitive sayings the humans use: these words condition their conscious and their subconscious minds into believing they can do something they earlier doubted was possible.

Your affectionate Mentor,
Shrewdtrap, S.C.
Department of Demonomics

From: Shrewdtrap@hellnet.edu
To: Warmwart@worldtrick.com
Subject: Corrupting Their Belief in Free Enterprise

My dear Warmwart:

On hotter nights down here I amuse myself by going through old files. Besides the distraction, this practice refreshes my recollection of our past strategies. "One who studies past mistakes and successes will avoid the former and repeat the latter."

Although we follow this axiom ourselves, we have had remarkable success, in modern times, convincing various groups of humans that *they* should not.

At any rate, I came across a Memorandum-to-File composed while the French Revolution was in its most gloriously gory phase. I also retrieved some Letters to various Tempters, including Slimerot, who is now working with excellent prospects we have in a Middle East terrorist group.

The file memo memorialized a meeting of the Future Bureau of the Joint Chiefs of the Low Command. Though things in France were roiling, we knew that eventually the carnage would end and the Enemy's agents in Europe would restore a measure of sanity.

Looking at the English-speaking world as a whole, we faced a peculiar problem with the British and the Americans: they had embraced some very unfortunate ideas of constitutional Due Process, Limited Government, and Free Enterprise.

Only a few of their writers--Adam Smith, Edmund Burke, and the American "Founding Fathers"--could explain these concepts. But the common people accepted them intuitively.

The people believed a man should keep the fruit of his labors ... pay low taxes ... run his own business ... honor contracts ... patent his inventions ... save for the future ... pass any wealth he built on to his children.

These harmful notions spread prosperity like a plague. In America especially, ordinary citizens used their freedom to create extraordinary prosperity.

So, in the environment of freedom, the practitioners of Free Enterprise gained economic control of their own lives and, for most of them, a high measure of personal fulfillment, i.e., a degree of happiness. As the people's standard of living increased, Economics lost its claim to being the Dismal Science.

As we left that meeting, I remarked to Slimerot that we needed a multi-pronged strategy to corrupt this Free Enterprise System before it got out of hand. I had two ideas in mind: on the macro level, trick human educators and opinion leaders into adopting an intellectual theory of Socialism.

I suggested we promote class envy ... urge the lie that when one man earns extra money his gain is some other man's loss, as if the static economic "pie" were always the same size, so that whenever one man eats a piece he leaves less for all the others.

Needless to say, in a productive society it is possible to "bake a bigger pie"--a truth we had to hide. I called this corruption of sound economic theory *Demonomics*, and the Joint Chiefs set up a Department on it.

An interruption. I am called to a joint meeting of our Department and the Department of Cultural Depravity.

Your affectionate Mentor,
Shrewdtrap, S.C.
Department of Demonomics

From: Shrewdtrap@hellnet.edu
To: Warmwart@worldtrick.com
Subject: A Job as the Road to Unhappiness

My dear Warmwart:

The meeting is over. I will return to my narrative.

My second idea was this: on the micro level, persuade individual humans always to pursue their financial destiny through a *job* rather than through *an equity position* in their own business.

In a job a person earns the average of what others would accept to replace him. If Joe has enthusiasm, honesty, creativity, discipline, willingness to learn, etc., he might be "worth" $20.00 per hour to Employer X. But if Tom, Dick, Harry, Mary, Joan, and Ann have these qualities but are willing to work for an average of $10.00 per hour, X will offer only $10.00.

Thus Joe will not earn proportionate reward for his extra hard work: rather, his income is "scaled down" to blend in with the group. He will never be paid "what he's worth."

Moreover, someone else controls his life. The Boss tells him when to arrive, what to wear, when he is hungry, when to go home. Indirectly, by controlling his income, he also tells him what kind of house to live in, car to drive, presents to give his wife, and college his children can attend.

Best of all, in their frantic competitive world, the Boss tells him how much time he can have to work out, to play golf, to enjoy being with his family.

I will postpone comment on the other benefits to teaching humans they should work for someone else rather than for themselves; may return to the point later.

Your affectionate Mentor,
Shrewdtrap, S.C.
Department of Demonomics

———

From: Shrewdtrap@hellnet.edu
To: Warmwart@worldtrick.com
Subject: Continuing the Narrative

My dear Warmwart:

I will return to recounting the meeting with Slimerot.

That master of duplicity Slimerot told me to my face that the first idea was absurd. To promote Socialism, he asserted, we would have to convince journalists ... clergymen ... professors ... that a centralized ant-hill society controlled from the top down would be more productive than a decentralized free society.

The problem was simply a matter of evidence and of truth: there had been no example in all human history where, through "central planning" by some governmental elite, a nation had spread wealth widely into what humans call the "middle class."

But there are plenty of examples where the elite--usually called oligarchy or nobility--monopolized the sources of wealth such as land and commerce, and made it nigh impossible for the average man or woman to join them.

So we would have to lie to the journalists, clergymen, and professors. Slimerot contended that they were too smart to be fooled by central planning claptrap. He convinced me that the Joint Chiefs would laugh at such an absurd strategy.

But later, without telling me, that hellish Slimerot sought a private audience with the Chiefs. Embellishing *my* idea with marginal gloss of his own, he convinced them to make it our main strategy for the Nineteenth Century. They even promoted him to chief ghost writer for Karl Marx and Frederick Engels!

When I learned how devilishly well Slimerot pirated *my* insight, I set in motion a devious whispering campaign against him. By the end of the Century, I got him transferred to the Czarist Secret Police, later the NKVD, eventually the KGB.

Indeed, to prove that *two* can lie to one's superiors, I managed to have him bottled up overseeing brainwashing chambers in the Lubianka. A pleasant enough place for fiends that feed on torture; but boring for a spirit like Slimerot, who itched to promote Marxism in American universities.

This account is for your eyes only, Warmwart, to spell out the lesson. Delete it from all files, folders, and computer drives.

But do not delete its lesson from memory: do not dare claim any success you might engineer, following my orders, as if it were your own. *I* will have the glory and the promotions. If you know what is good for you, keep in mind who is

Your affectionate Mentor,
Shrewdtrap, S.C.
Department of Demonomics

From: Shrewdtrap@hellnet.edu
To: Warmwart@worldtrick.com
Subject: He Needs Only a Few

My dear Warmwart:

I will return to the practical side of my counsel. There is only so much philosophy a sophomoric intellect can absorb.

So two of the eight new people are incubating. Of the remaining six, two are buying products on the website but doing little else.

But four have put together fairly long lists of people they know and are letting McDermott and Frank help them with phone calls, to set up meetings. And you think this is progress for *us*!

Warmwart, how long have you been observing humans? Don't you understand that to some extent, business success is a statistical thing, a *numbers game...?*

How many cars drive by the local Shell station without buying gas or going into for a tune-up? Hundreds more than come in.

How many humans walk a mall "window-shopping" and enter a shop and yet do not buy anything there? Far more than buy.

How many mail solicitations go out to possible customers, compared to the number of recipients who act on the solicitation? If the mailer achieves a mere 3% positive response, his mailing worked.

The gas station owner, the shopkeeper, the mail-order businessman do not dwell on how many people did *not* jump at the chance to buy their product or service.

All they care about is whether an adequate *small minority* of those who *could* buy, *do* buy. Usually that is as few as one out of ten. Sometimes merely one out of a hundred.

Here, if Frank located merely *one* committed individual or couple out of the twelve who more or less got "in," his meeting would have been a success. If he finds just one *per year* who duplicates McDermott, in due time he will earn a six-figure income.

Here, of twelve who looked at the program, four are willing to do it--unless you get sharper and deflect them. In their business, one out of three is a good percentage.

So don't be so pleased with yourself.

Your affectionate Mentor,
Shrewdtrap, S.C.
Department of Demonomics

———————

From: Shrewdtrap@hellnet.edu
To: Warmwart@worldtrick.com
Subject: No Rewards for Failure

My dear Warmwart:

So, despite your best efforts to increase stress in their lives, Frank and spouse are more focussed than ever. He has established a rhythm; he contacts one or two new people per day, he calls two per day, he shows the program four times a week, and with McDermott he "works depth" in three "legs" each week.

You cannot think of a thing to do about this! Between the lines, I discern a sniveling entreaty for a different assignment.

We do not reward failure. I have a better idea than your hint that you would like to promote more wasteful government spending on boondoggle projects that only make social problems worse. Sorry. We have more than enough humans doing our job for us in that field. We do not need any more tempters there.

Here is the better idea: you can "work depth" yourself. Go down the line of people entering Frank's business. Single out the ones who fail to grasp the importance of the System. Look for those who are not trying to get to know McDermott and his terrible wife Maryann. Locate the procrastinators.

Then take these flaws and intensify them. Whatever little weaknesses they have you can magnify. If need be, arrange for some pitchman for another business to run into them and make the case why he has "a better deal."

Like antelope on the African grasslands vulnerable to a lion prowling around in search of his next meal, their own weaknesses or the outsider with a supposedly better deal can cut them off from the herd. Then they will be more vulnerable to our attacks.

It appears to be too late to stop Frank from attacking the challenge with firm consistency. But if we can cut down the herd of people he is building, his profit and his success will take longer. It will take more time.

Time is on the side of those who use it.

Your affectionate Mentor,
Shrewdtrap, S.C.
Department of Demonomics

From: Shrewdtrap@hellnet.edu
To: Warmwart@worldtrick.com
Subject: Pressures in Their Lives

My dear Warmwart:

At last! Some good news!

You tell me that Jennifer has some problems with her pregnancy, and her doctor wants to severely restrict her activities. It may come to the point that she spends the next couple months in bed.

At the same time, Frank has sponsored some people in a city three hours away—a "distance group," more or less. Helping them will swallow a good deal of what little spare time he has.

I see considerable pressure building in their lives, even without you.

Send me a Memo on your plans.

Your affectionate Mentor,
Shrewdtrap, S.C.
Department of Demonomics

From: Shrewdtrap@hellnet.edu
To: Warmwart@worldtrick.com
Subject: Dumb Plans

What!! You think one of your options is to haunt Frank and Jennifer's house ... rattle shutters ... hurl coffee cups against walls ... move chairs out of place ... and generally frighten her while she's home alone!

Such theatrics are not worthy of sophisticated tempters like us here at Demonomics. The poltergeist battalion is headquartered in Europe. Do you want me to demote you to a menial position with them?

Come up with better options. Right away.

Your affectionate Mentor,
Shrewdtrap, S.C.
Department of Demonomics

From: Shrewdtrap@hellnet.edu
To: Warmwart@worldtrick.com
Subject: Avoid the Paralysis of Analysis

My dear Warmwart:

While you were frozen in thought again, your opponents acted. That terrible Maryann McDermott started to help Jennifer with the child, bring her meals, go so far as to clean her house.

Meantime, McDermott is driving the three hours to the distant city every other week to explain the program, so that Frank can spend those evenings with Jennifer.

And all you could ask, in your comments to me, is: why the humans would go out of their way to *help* someone else when there is nothing immediate in it for them?

Even I have no clear idea. Despite our best teaching, some of them seem to be "unselfish." Sludgespit and others of our best researchers have analyzed the concept for eons and they still cannot break its code.

But it does not matter. The point for *you* is to salvage whatever you can in this situation. Despite help from the McDermotts, Frank and Jennifer are still under pressure. Find ways to leverage that pressure into business failure.

Stay on track. But don't think so much unless you come up with a thought you can act on!

> Your affectionate Mentor,
> Shrewdtrap, S.C.
> Department of Demonomics

From: Shrewdtrap@hellnet.edu
To: Warmwart@worldtrick.com
Subject: The Law of Sowing and Reaping

My dear Warmwart:

You asked me whether there is some way to know, automatically, as it were, which direction to tempt humans to go, when they have multiple options.

The question brings up some deep issues that may be beyond your mental powers to grasp. Still, I will proceed on the assumption that you are as smart as some of the humans you have tempted over the eons. Because some humans have understood the principles I will explain, it may be that you can as well.

The humans' universe is governed by Principles. There is the Principle of Noncontradiction: "A thing cannot both be, and not be, at the same time and in the same way." Thus a man cannot tell an objective truth and an objective lie at the same time. A thing cannot be both wet and dry at the same time.

On the physical level, there is the Principle of Growth: "A living being must grow or it will decline and die." A corollary is that once a being--say, a human athlete--has grown to his full development, he must continue to exercise, or he will decline and weaken. "Use it or lose it," the humans say.

On the level of the rules of nature, there is the Law of Gravity: "All beings with weight are pulled toward the earth at a certain rapid speed." Nor does the flight of airplanes negate this law; rather, they use another law, that wind across a wing of a certain shape causes enough upward air pressure to overcome gravity.

[The Law of Gravity does not apply to us spirits; but sometimes we use it when we deal with humans: e.g., convince them, under the influence of drugs, that the Law of Gravity does not apply to them.]

At this point, I will answer your question directly, by commenting on the key Principle that your targets have learned: the Principle of Sowing and Reaping.

A farmer must sow seeds before he reaps a harvest. A would-be doctor must study medicine before he practices medicine. A runner must train before he wins races. And if a man enters his cold house equipped with a wood stove and says to it, "Wood stove, give me heat," the answer would be, "First give me logs."

So, the first element of the Principle of Sowing and Reaping is obvious: one must *put in* before he can *take out*.

In their Internet business, McDermott and Frank must help others-- and this includes putting in time and money *for* others [purchase of books and tapes, attending seminars, travel to explain the program, phone calls]- *-before* they can receive time and money for themselves.

You may be surprised to learn that many people join multilevel businesses and expect to take profit out before they have invested any time, money, or effort into their business.

There are two other aspects that are less obvious. Besides the fact that one must reap *later* than when he sows, he also will reap *more* than what he sowed; and quite often he will reap *in a different place* than where he sowed.

As to the first point, recall my E-mail to you on apple orchards and duplication: in due time a dozen seeds can produce a few hundred apples. As to the second, if a bird swallows some of the seeds he may release them miles away, where a few apple trees may spring up quite distant from the sower.

Unless you interfere, McDermott and Frank may well keep on "sowing," and--unless you teach them impatience--they will not let delay in reaping a harvest discourage them; and before they fade out, some of those they bring in will give them a good referral--a "harvest" elsewhere.

If people obey these Principles, their lives generally are happier. Thus we must motivate them to disobey the Principles. When disobeyed, the Law of Sowing leads them to want the results without doing the work that produces the results. They want heat from the wood stove, without giving it logs.

I'd say that every thief rejects this Principle. Rather than work to earn the money to buy a car, which takes time, he simply steals it, an act which takes mere moments. Our Principle of Immediate Self-Gratification is the antithesis of the Principle of Sowing and Reaping.

All in all, Warmwart, *your* working Principle should be: first, identify the Principle they should follow, for their natural happiness; second, tempt them toward the opposite.

With the people in Frank and McDermott's group, teach them to pursue immediate self-gratification.

> Your affectionate Mentor,
> Shrewdtrap, S.C.
> Department of Demonomics

From: Shrewdtrap@hellnet.edu
To: Warmwart@worldtrick.com
Subject: Two Kinds of Anger

My dear Warmwart:

You tell me Frank is getting angry. On the face of it, this is good. Anger leads to harsh words, destructive acts, frayed friendships. Anger is a gas station on the road to irrational conduct.

But there can be creative anger: the kind a man channels into renewed commitment, firmer purpose, disciplined performance. This is rational anger.

Unlike ourselves--*we* maintain permanent seething anger, like a pot of water on a stove set on "medium high"--humans usually cannot sustain intensity of anger. But for a while, their anger can move them to bursts of almost superhuman effort.

Tell me, is Frank's anger rational or irrational?

Your affectionate Mentor,
Shrewdtrap, S.C.
Department of Demonomics

From: Shrewdtrap@hellnet.edu
To: Warmwart@worldtrick.com
Subject: Using Frank's Irritations

My dear Warmwart:

I could have guessed. Frank is rational. Most attorneys are, even when they are angry.

So what is he angry about? You say it is a number of different related things. One is the slowness, as he perceives it, of the growth of his business.

To profit by his present discontent, you could remind him of someone who has reached a highly profitable level in, say, ninety days. Tell him *he* must be doing something wrong, or that McDermott is not letting him in on "the secret."

Of course, since you have allowed him and McDermott to become close friends, this ploy may not drive a wedge between them. McDermott will probably say something like, "The view from the top is just as good for those who take longer to climb the mountain."

Or, McDermott might remark, "I didn't do it in ninety days, either. But I did it. My sponsor told me to stop comparing myself to others, and just keep on doing what I was doing." Then he will mention an attorney in Illinois who took five years but today earns far more, part time, than he did putting in seventy/eighty hours a week in his law practice.

In any event, you say the other matter that irritates him is that "people who should know better" sometimes reject the business. He has in mind one of his law partners, who is just as time-bankrupt as Frank, but seems not to mind that his children scarcely know him and his wife is beginning to resent him.

Suggest to Frank that it must be *his* fault that this fellow could be led to water but still, like the proverbial horse, will not think. Don't let him entertain the truths that some people do not want to admit they need to change, and that motivation is an "inside job," by which I mean: Frank can't motivate his partner.

67

Finally, you say his anger has driven him to work harder. He wants to prove to McDermott he can do this thing, and he wants to say, "I told you so," to the partner who won't listen.

Try to calm him down. Tell him anger ill befits a deliberative attorney. Tell him it raises his blood pressure. Anything to get him to walk where he could run.

Your affectionate Mentor,
Shrewdtrap, S.C.
Department of Demonomics

From: Shrewdtrap@hellnet.edu
To: Warmwart@worldtrick.com
Subject: Success through Spamming

My dear Warmwart:

So his group has exploded, has it? He brought in nine people in two months. Each of these sponsored a few, and, with those adding some, he now has over forty people in his business group.

What do you want from me, sympathy?

Needless to say, you won't get it. Sympathy is not part of my nature. But I have a suggestion.

Tell those people all they need to do is look for geeks and nerds who want to sit at their computer at 2:00 a.m. in their pajamas, and--supposedly--get rich. Tell them the Internet will do it all. Tell them income from E-Commerce is automatic, self-generating, spontaneous. Click in, and the money pours out.

Twist the whole program into a plausible "get-rich-quick" scheme. Tell them to send out E-mails to every person on every list they can buy. This is called "spamming." It will probably get them into big trouble.

Even if they control their misplaced eagerness to spam, and limit their unsolicited E-mails to people they actually know, they will not automatically sponsor 50 people with 50 E-mails.

This business you are trying to disrupt is still based on *personal relationships*. By and large, they will have to meet and "get to know" the people to whom they offer the business. They have to find out their Dreams and, as much as one can in a few initial meetings, create confidence in the new person that they will indeed help them succeed.

Sending out a flock of E-mails does not prove much. But driving three hours to do a presentation at the new person's relatives' house is persuasive evidence that they will work to help them.

So, nudge them toward substituting exclusive computer involvement for intensive personal involvement. The thing is two dimensional; friendships are, psychologically, three dimensional.

When their misplaced reliance on the computer alone to build the business leads to momentary failure, being part of the Microwave Generation, they will probably quit.

Your affectionate Mentor,
Shrewdtrap, S.C.
Department of Demonomics

From: Shrewdtrap@hellnet.edu
To: Warmwart@worldtrick.com
Subject: Unfortunate Developments

My dear Warmwart:

You have been silent for over a month and the pressures of other tasks have kept me from sending a Demand-for-Report letter.

But, as you know, we have other operatives in the field on all fronts. Even though their assignments prevent them from aiding resident tempters such as yourself, they do report back on your activities. One of them is Smearsneak, who has worked successfully in our Political Division in the Capital.

Smearsneak has reported the following unfortunate developments: Jennifer's pregnancy is back on a healthy track; McDermott and Frank have identified six "legs" which have other leaders "below" them working the business with the same intensity as McD. & F.; three of those "legs" are just about to reach "critical mass."

When that happens, Frank will have positioned himself to earn, from this business, about eighty percent of what his law practice pulls in. This means he is within striking distance of retirement, if he wants. And before he is forty years old!

I assume you informed me of none of these developments because they make you look like a punch-drunk fighter about to be knocked out. And by humans, to boot!

Can you think of nothing to derail his train? Or are you going to stand there and let it run you over?

Your affectionate Mentor,
Shrewdtrap, S.C.
Department of Demonomics

From: Shrewdtrap@hellnet.edu
To: Warmwart@worldtrick.com
Subject: Back to the Law of Sowing and Reaping

My dear Warmwart:

No, I cannot go over old ground with new words. If you want a refresher on a basic Principle that I have already explained, go to your archive file and retrieve my earlier commentary on the Principle of Sowing and Reaping.

It is still pertinent, both for dealing with the humans and for assessing your future. You too will reap from what you have--or have not--sown.

Here's the good news: your future has been entirely in your own hands. Here's the bad news: your future has been entirely in your own hands.

So, even as the game winds down, you had better score some points!

> Your affectionate Mentor,
> Shrewdtrap, S.C.
> Department of Demonomics

From: Shrewdtrap@hellnet.edu
To: Warmwart@worldtrick.com
Subject: Recognition

My dear Warmwart:

So they stood there on stage, did they, before a thousand people. And they received lavish--you said fulsome--praise for their accomplishment. And you hovered in the wings and gloated that somehow, you know not how, your skills brought them into what you call this Orgy of Pride.

Warmwart, once again you have missed the point! Perhaps the new people in the audience thought the applause was excessive, but I would expect greater insight from a tempter under *my* guidance.

So--once again--I will take up my valuable time to explain to you some basics in human psychology.

Humans need a measure of recognition or appreciation for their work. In a way, this is food for the ego just as meat and potatoes are food for their bodies. And on a deeper philosophical level, it may well be a matter of Justice: approval is part of the *payment* for their efforts.

In the modern world, except for the field of sports, the expression of this natural approval for accomplishment by one's peers is rare. The spectators applaud; but men on other teams must strain to express enthusiasm for a competitor's success.

In the working world of corporations and universities and hospitals and government agencies, peer approval [except at the token retirement party] hardly ever happens. When does the Dean convene the Faculty for a party to celebrate the promotion of Professor X to Tenure? Never!

When does the head Deputy in Charge of Deputies in the Federal Government have an hour-long meeting to celebrate Mr. Y's advancement from GS-12 to GS-13 ... and then give him a chance to tell his story, i.e., tell how he did it? Never! The assembled GS-ers of lower rank would gag on their own jealousy.

For that matter, when does a wife call all the children together for an evening celebration with Dad as the Guest of Honor, to praise him for all his work that month, or applaud his achieving Tenure or GS-13 rank? Only if the promotion came the same week as his birthday.

There are exceptions, of course. In the insurance industry, for example, the year's Top Producer usually receives on-stage recognition from the company President, while the assembled brothers and sisters in sales applaud with a measure of genuine appreciation.

Note that insurance sales people are entrepreneurs. People with *jobs* rarely are feted. Insurance sales entrepreneurs can "go and do likewise." Their success--and recognition--depend on their own efforts. They can join the charmed circle of success by learning how to do it right and then do more of it.

But by and large, people with jobs cannot advance solely by their own efforts. "Office politics," nepotism, personality clashes, and other subjective factors unrelated to performance quite often block the advancement and recognition they deserve.

The leaders of the top multilevel networking businesses understand all this. So their System includes the very important on-stage recognition of their members who have reached progressive stages of business growth. And Frank and Jennifer stumbled into the best of all these businesses.

When Frank and Jennifer walked on stage to a standing ovation, and Steve and that outrageously good Maryann McDermott lifted up their arms in the winner's gesture of success in combat, *you* ignorantly congratulated yourself that they were wallowing in the quicksand of Pride.

Not so. My guess is that Frank and Jennifer actually felt sentiments of that peculiar thing called *humility*. They did not climb the mountain alone. They had Steve and that awful woman Maryann setting the pace and pulling them up; they had a hundred people in their group pushing them on. And they knew it.

And the applause was not hypocritical, though I am sure you wish it were. Every person in that audience is also an entrepreneur: each realizes they can climb the same road up to success as did the evening's guests of honor.

So stop the self-congratulation. *They* reached a milestone in their journey; *you* achieved nothing. Maybe I should reassign you to the office of some Deputy in Charge of Deputies in the Government, where your flawed grasp of human motivation would do less harm to our Cause.

Your affectionate Mentor,
Shrewdtrap, S.C.
Department of Demonomics

P.S.: In light of your non-accomplishments shadowing your targets in business, I am hereby reassigning you to our Poltergeist Division. Demonomics will be better in your absence. Report in one minute to Shockspur on the moors in northern England.

But before you do, delete all records of my E-mail correspondence with you. I want no evidence of what certain negative spirits among the Joint Chiefs might deem my incompetence.